This book belongs to:

....

PETER PAN

PUBLISHED BY PETER HADDOCK LIMITED,
BRIDLINGTON, ENGLAND
PRINTED IN ITALY

ISBN 07105 0245 1

This is the story of Peter Pan. He is the little boy who never grew up. His constant companion is Tinker Bell, the fairy from Never-Never Land. They have lots of marvellous adventures together. In this story they take the Darling children with them.

The Darling family live in London. They are Mr. & Mrs. Darling and their three children. Wendy is the eldest child and she has two brothers named John and Michael. They are very happy children and are always dreaming of exciting adventures.

One night, just as the children are preparing for bed, Peter Pan and Tinker Bell appear at the bedroom window. He asks the children to fly with them to Never-Never Land to meet his friends, the Lost Boys. However, the children cannot fly but Tinker Bell has magic powers and she can teach them. So, with the aid of Tinker Bell, they fly out of the window and soar high up into the sky. On and on they fly until they see below them Never-Never Land. They can also see Captain Hook's ship anchored in the bay. Captain Hook is Peter Pan's most hated enemy.

When Peter Pan and the children arrive on Never-Never Land, they have to hurry to Peter Pan's hideout before Captain Hook sees them. The hideout is at the foot of a hollow tree and it is here that the children meet the Lost Boys.

Peter Pan leaves Michael and John to play with the Lost Boys and takes Wendy to the Mermaid's Lagoon. From here they can see Captain Hook in his boat. He has taken Tiger Lily prisoner. Tiger Lily is the daughter of the Red Indian Chief Sitting Bull and is one of Peter Pan's greatest friends.

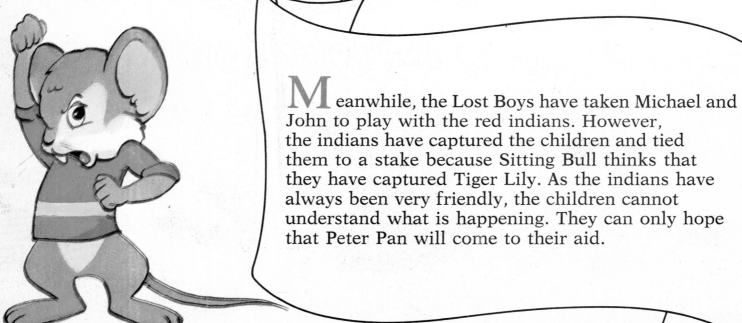

Meanwhile, the Lost Boys have taken Michael and John to play with the red indians. However, the indians have captured the children and tied them to a stake because Sitting Bull thinks that they have captured Tiger Lily. As the indians have always been very friendly, the children cannot understand what is happening. They can only hope that Peter Pan will come to their aid.

Tiger Lily, in the meantime, cannot escape from the cruel Captain Hook. He has tied her to a rock and will not set her free unless she will tell him where Peter Pan's secret hideout is. She will surely be drowned when the water rises at high tide.

Luckily, Peter Pan does arrive in time and he and Captain Hook fight a furious duel. Tiger Lily watches anxiously, and is very relieved when Captain Hook is beaten. Peter Pan quickly frees Tiger Lily before the water rises any further. Peter Pan, Wendy and Tiger Lily board a raft and set sail for the shore. They leave Captain Hook in the water, and as you can imagine, he is not at all pleased.

When the three children arrive back at the Indian camp, Chief Sitting Bull is so pleased to see Tiger Lily back home safely that he receives Peter Pan with full honours. He, of course, releases Peter Pan's friends as he now knows that they did not kidnap Tiger Lily.

Captain Hook has now discovered that Tinker Bell is jealous of Wendy and he tries to make her tell him where Peter Pan's hideout is. Eventually, she gives in to Captain Hook, but before she discloses the whereabouts of the hideout she makes Captain Hook promise that no harm will come to Peter Pan.

Immediately they have obtained this information, Captain Hook's pirates go to the hideout. They capture Wendy and her brothers and the Lost Children. Before they know what is happening all the children are carried back to Captain Hook's ship.

Captain Hook is very cunning. He leaves a parcel containing a bomb in the hideout. His idea is that when Peter Pan arrives home and sees the parcel, he will open it. Then, of course, it will explode and kill him.

F ortunately, Tinker Bell realises that she has been tricked by Captain Hook. He had broken his promise not to harm Peter Pan. She hurries to save her friend. With great courage she removes the parcel from the hideout and flys away with it.

The bomb explodes but luckily Tinker Bell is not hurt. When Peter Pan sees the explosion he races to the scene. He finds Tinker Bell in the rubble and pulls her to safety. He is so happy to find her alive that he confesses that he loves her more than anything else in the world.

On board Captain Hook's ship, the pirates try to force Wendy and her friends to work as cabin boys. They refuse, and as punishment, Wendy is thrown into the sea. She would surely have drowned if Peter Pan had not arrived and helped her to safety. Now that Peter Pan and Tinker Bell have joined the other children on the ship, they band together to fight the pirates. They are very brave and fight fiercely.

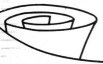Suddenly, Peter Pan and Captain Hook find themselves face to face. They fight another fierce duel and Peter Pan forces Captain Hook into a very precarious position, hanging on to the mast by his hook. Captain Hook desperately tries to hold on to his position because if he falls he will drop straight into the sea. He knows only too well that there is a crocodile in the lagoon. Eventually, however, he cannot hold on any longer and he falls into the sea.

The crocodile is overjoyed when Captain Hook falls into the water. Once in a duel, Peter Pan had sliced off Captain Hook's hand and fed it to the crocodile and ever since then the crocodile had been waiting to finish him off. Now he does just that and at last Peter Pan's most bitter enemy is dead.
Peter Pan takes pity on the pirates and lets them go free. They are so afraid that he will throw them to the crocodile that they promise they will never harm anyone again. Peter Pan is now captain of the ship and he sets sail for London to return Wendy and her brothers to their home.

The ship arrives safely in London. Here Peter Pan explains to the children that they cannot accompany Tinker Bell and himself on any more of their adventures. After saying a sad goodbye to their friends, Peter Pan and Tinker Bell once more return to Never-Never Land.

So now Wendy, John and Michael are back in their bedroom in London where the whole adventure started. They are very sad that they will not see Peter Pan and Tinker Bell again, but they all agree that they will never forget the exciting time they have had. They could never have imagined such a story.